Princess Poems

By Clare Bevan

Illustrated by Lara Jones

MACMILLAN CHILDREN'S BOOKS

For All the Lovely Ladies in Crowthorne's Coffee Shop. And for Gaby, the Princess of Macmillan Castle.

First published 2005
by Macmillan Children's Books
a division of Macmillan Publishers Limited
20 New Wharf Road, London N1 9RR
Basingstoke and Oxford
www.panmacmillan.com

Associated companies throughout the world

ISBN 0 330 43389 X

Text copyright © Clare Bevan 2005
Illustrations copyright © Lara Jones 2005

The right of Clare Bevan and Lara Jones to be identified as the
author and illustrator of this book has been asserted by them in accordance
with the Copyright, Designs and Patents Act 1988.

1 3 5 7 9 8 6 4 2

A CIP catalogue record for this book is available from the British Library.
Printed by Mackays of Chatham plc, Chatham, Kent.

Contents

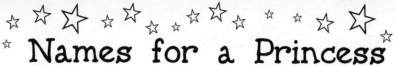

Names for a Princess

Clare found this useful list wrapped around a silver spoon.

A Princess should have an
   unusual name
That plays in your mind like a
   musical game.

Karamalinda,
Tangly-Hair,
Rozamatina,
Lacey-the-Fair.

Marzana Mazey,
Star-of-the-Skies,
Dorinda Daisy,
Emerald-Eyes.

Little Cozetta,
Ebony-Locks,
Shy Sarabetta
Fifi-de-Fox.

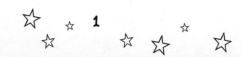

Tiger Truella,
Pearl-from-the-Sea,
Silvery Bella,
Sweet Annalee.

A Princess should have a
    remarkable name,
That glows in your mind like a
    flickering flame.

The Magic Map

Clare found this little scroll in a forgotten cupboard.

Through the magic garden,
Round the magic well,
Hear the magic statues
Speak their magic spell,
Find the magic fountain,
Hug the magic tree,
Walk the magic pathway,
Twist the magic key,
Search the magic castle,
Climb the magic stair,
Watch the magic princess
Comb her magic hair,
Steal the magic apple
From its magic dish
And ask the magic mirror
To grant your magic wish.

Ten Things a Real Princess Can Do

This little list was found under Clare's feather bed.

1. She can grow her hair as long (and as strong) as a ladder.
2. She can sleep for a hundred years without ever sneezing.
3. She can feel a single, tiny pea under a mountain of feathers.
4. She can find the only spinning wheel in the whole castle.
5. She can always spot a REAL prince, even if his clothes are torn by thorns or scorched by grumpy dragons.
6. She can turn a frog into a handsome prince, although he may have rather large feet.
7. She can dance until midnight in shiny, glass slippers (which is harder than you may think).
8. She can sew bundles of stinging nettles into soft, green shirts.
9. She can talk to her magic mirror (although she doesn't always believe what it says).

10. She can make her Ugly Sisters faint
with surprise (but still remember to
invite them to her wedding).

The Princess's Treasures

Clare found this poem rolled up inside a rather scruffy rug.

The Princess owned a whole turret of
   treasures.

There was a toy dragon that breathed real
   sparks,
A necklace made from the stony tears of
   statues,
A wooden unicorn that danced on a lawn
   of green glass,
A casket of blue shells from a mermaid's
   cave
And a tiny spinning wheel
That could turn spider silk into birdsong.

Yet the thing she loved the best
Was a scruffy crimson rug.

Its patterns had been stolen by the desert
   sun,
Its fringes had been frayed by ice storms,
Its tufts had been flattened by sleeping
   tigers,
But still it rippled across her room
Like an ancient, flying fish,
And when it slept beside her bed
It smelled of spices
And meadow flowers
And salty seas.

A Few Frightening Things

Clare found this poem in the bucket of a haunted well.

These are the things a Princess fears ...

Broken mirrors,
Dragon tears,
Poisoned apples,
Wicked wands,

Slimy frogs
In slimy ponds,
Rusty keys
For creaky locks,

Stinging nettles,
Silent clocks,
Sharpened combs
By haunted wells,
Spinning wheels
And cruel spells,

Sleeping for
A hundred years . . .

These are the things a Princess fears.

The Three Princesses of Cloud Castle

Clare saw this poem scribbled across a cloudy sky.

If you gaze at the morning sky
You'll see Cloud Castle drifting by.

The smallest princess
Is golden as dawn,
She sleeps like a dormouse,
She wakes with a yawn,
She's soft as a whisper,
She's shy as a fawn.

If you follow the kestrel's cry
You'll see Cloud Castle far and high.

The middle princess
Is fierce as the sun,
Her temper is hot
And is swiftly begun,
Her smiles burn like cinders,
She's frightened of none.

If you search where the breezes sigh
You'll see Cloud Castle fade and fly.

The tallest princess
Is dark as the night,
Her starry eyes sparkle
With laughter and light,
Her skirts whirl as wildly
As bat wings in flight.

If you wish it, and if you try,
You'll see Cloud Castle by and by.

Step by Step

Clare found this poem drawn in the dust on a spiral staircase.

Tiptoe, tiptoe, Up the spiral stair, If you hear a wicked laugh, Do take care!

Stumble, stumble, On the spiral stair, If you see a spinning wheel, Do beware!

Tumble, tumble, Down the spiral stair, If you sleep a hundred years, Don't despair!

A Visit to the Palace Museum

Here's a tiny, glass slipper,
Snow White's golden comb,
A rose that was stolen
From Beast's lonely home,
A nasty, sharp spindle,
A pea (slightly squashed),
A nettle-leaf shirt
(Which has never been washed),
A hair from Rapunzel
(Incredibly long),
A swan's magic feather,
The words of a song
That was sung by a dragon,
A frog's little crown,
A pumpkin (with windows),
A raggy, old gown,
And a casket of shells
From the King of the Sea . . .
But the LOVELIEST treasure
(I think you'll agree)
Is the beautiful, beautiful
Picture of ME.

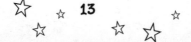

Cinderella's Dress

Clare heard someone singing this poem in the kitchen one night.

The kitchen mice sing as they run, run, run,
"We will spin the sparkle of the sun, sun, sun.

We will spy lost treasures in the town,
   town, town,
We will find nine buttons for her gown,
   gown, gown.

We will take blue feathers from a bed, bed,
   bed,
We will ask the spiders for their thread,
   thread, thread.

We will catch the colours of the skies,
   skies, skies,
We will match the dazzle of her eyes, eyes,
   eyes.

We will steal the ripples of the seas, seas,
   seas,
We will add the rustle of the trees, trees, trees.

We will snip the flowers from the grass,
grass, grass.
We will make two slippers out of glass,
glass, glass.

We will sew the starlight in her hair, hair,
hair,
We will weave a wonder that is rare, rare,
rare.

And Cinderella shall be rich, rich, rich."
The kitchen mice sing as they stitch, stitch,
stitch.

Counting Rhyme for a Young Princess

Clare found this rhyme under a bundle of royal arithmetic books.

12 Naughty girls, dancing on their toes.
11 Wild swans, white as winter snows.
10 Beds of feathers for a REAL princess.
 9 Silver buttons on a golden dress.
 8 Tiny mice, stitching tiny stitches.
 7 Kindly dwarfs, sharing all their riches.
 6 Lonely years in Rapunzel's tower.
 5 Witch's fingers, full of wicked power.
 4 Twisty pathways (one will lead to glory).
 3 Magic wishes in a bedtime story.
 2 Ugly sisters, angry and alarming.
 1 Little slipper and one Prince Charming.

The Twisty Path

Clare found this poem pinned to a wooden signpost.

The Princess wished for riches
For ever and a day.
"Then you must choose your magic path,"
I heard a fairy say.

The signpost said: TO GLORY.
TO FAME. TO FORTUNE RARE.
The Princess chose the twisty path
That led to: WHO KNOWS WHERE?

She found a ruby apple
Beneath an emerald tree,
She found a sunset streaked with gold
Above a sapphire sea.

She found a silver fountain
Where icy jewels grew,
She found a pearly bracelet made
From early-morning dew.

She found a rainbow necklace
Reflected in a brook,
She found a precious treasure with
Each lucky step she took.

The Princess wished for riches
For ever and a day.
"She chose the path to HAPPINESS,"
I heard a fairy say.

TO GLORY
10 MILES

The Twelve Dancing Princesses

(And the Crafty Soldier)

Clare found this poem inside a royal rowing boat.

"Who," yelled the King, "can tell me and
  say
Why my twelve dear daughters are weary
  all day?

And how can it be, that each bright dawn
Their dancing slippers are tattered and
  torn?"

A tall prince tried, but he slept with a
  snore –
Their dancing slippers were tattered once
  more.

A brave prince tried, but he dreamed of
  rain –
Their dancing slippers were tattered again.

A wise prince tried, but he dreamed of
  frost –
Their dancing slippers were hidden or lost.

A soldier tried. He said with a frown,
"I'll learn their secret. I'll track them
  down."

He wore a witch's invisible coat,
He saw them sail in a magical boat . . .

To a land where they danced the whole
  night through!
He told the King – and the daughters too.

So did he marry the clever princess
Who wore the loveliest, lavender dress?

Or did he decide on the youngest one
Whose smile was sweet as a sugar bun?

Or the gentle girl who (right from the
  start)
Whispered his name and captured his
  heart?

Frog Song

Clare heard this song one night beside her garden pond.

I wish she would kiss me
When waterweeds quiver.

I wish she would love me
When waves softly shiver.

I won't be a prince with
A palace to give her,

But I WILL be the handsomest
Frog in the river.

The Eleven Swans

Clare found this poem amongst a clump of stinging nettles.

Did you hear of the Princess
Whose brothers (they say)
Were changed into swans
Every dawn, every day?

Did you hear how she worked
(Without songs, without words)
To rescue those brothers,
Those poor, spellbound birds?

Did you hear how she wove
(Without minding the pain)
The nettle-leaf shirts
That would free them again?

Did you hear how her enemies
Said she must die?
(Though her Prince wept with grief
As the sun brushed the sky.)

Did you hear how she flung
Over feather and beak
Her magical shirts?
(And at last she could speak!)

Did you hear how one sleeve
Was a tangle of string?
(So the best of her brothers
Kept one snowy wing.)

Did you hear how the Princess
Was loved, and lived long
With her Prince and her brothers,
Her words and her song.

If You Were a Princess

Clare found this poem inside a big, golden pumpkin.

If YOU were a princess, what would YOU
  ride?

> A small, metal dragon
> With cogwheels inside?
> A horse with white feathers
> And hooves of black glass?
> A silvery unicorn
> Pounding the grass?

A fluttering carpet
That chases the bats?
A big, golden pumpkin
With coachmen like rats?
A castle that sways
On an elephant's back?
A long, steamy train
Going clickety clack?
Or a ship with blue sails
And YOUR name on the side?

If YOU were a princess, what would YOU
ride?

The Tiny Princess

Clare found this poem outside a rather smart mouse hole.

The King and Queen wished every day
For a little girl of their very own,
But when they found her amongst the
  bluebells
She was tinier than a sparrow's child
And her cries were no louder than a
  squeak.

They placed her inside half a walnut shell
Lined with dandelion fluff,
And they wrapped her in shawls
Woven by money spiders.
Even when she grew old enough
For ball gowns and glittering crowns
The Royal Toy Maker stitched and glued
  them all.

Yet the people were proud of their tiny
    Princess,
And when she married her handsome
    Mouse Prince
They locked up their cats
And leaned from their windows
To cheer and sing
In happy whispers.

The Sandcastle

Clare found this poem inside a striped seaside bucket.

In it came, the terrible tide,
"It will crush our castle!" the children
  cried.

Behind the walls
The servants ran –
The cooks, the maids
And the jester man.
"We will all be drowned."
They wailed and wept
As the waters dashed
And splashed and swept
The sandy turrets
Away, away.
But I heard the Princess
Laugh and say,
"Jump in my beautiful
Seashell boat!"
And I watched her sail
And I watched her float
Across the stormy
The salty waves
To the rocky shores
Of the Mermaid Caves.

While the children called (to hide their
    sorrow)
"We will build your castle again.
    Tomorrow!"

The Secret

Clare's pen wrote this poem by itself.

What makes a Princess
The rarest of girls?
Is it her casket
Of rubies and pearls?

Is it her throne,
Or her pink, pointy crown?
Is it her beautiful
Butterfly gown?

Is it her hair
So incredibly long?
Is it her dragon,
So scaly and strong?

Is it the Prince,
Who is eager to save her?
Is it the gift
That the Good Fairy gave her?

Or is it a secret
Too precious to tell?
And is there a chance
I'm a Princess as well?

The Tale of Princess Raven Wing

Clare discovered this tale between the pages of a long-lost book.

This tale is told
In a long-lost rhyme,
In a long-lost book,
From a far-off time.

Her eyes were as grey as a raven's wing,
She could not speak and she could not
     sing,
But around her throat on a silver string
Hung a rusty key and a ruby ring.

She dressed in shadows each winter night,
She searched the woods in the moon's cold
   light
For a tower of stones all ghostly white,
As the silver cord grew tight, grew tight.

At last she found the tower of stones,
Bright and bare as a witch's bones,
The door flew wide with weary groans.
She saw one cage, two empty thrones.

"Oh, hear my cry," a sad voice sighed.
"With wicked chains my cage is tied.
Will no one dare to step inside?
Will no one be my own true bride?"

She could not speak, she could not say,
And yet she would not run away.
She stepped across the floor so grey,
And in the dust she wrote, "I'll stay."

At once she heard a magic bell,
It broke the cord, it broke the spell,
And faster than there's time to tell,
Her key unlocked the cage as well.

She wears her ancient ruby ring,
She's learned to speak again, and sing.
She's found her dear, enchanted king –

So ends the tale of Raven Wing.

Kisses

Clare found this poem on the seat beside her garden pond.

Kisses (in stories)
Do marvellous things –
Turn frogs into princes,
Or beasts into kings,
Break evil enchantments,
Wake sleepers from dreams,
Make wicked old witches
Scream TERRIBLE screams.

Kisses (in stories)
Are awfully clever –
But I WON'T kiss a frog.
Not today. And not EVER!

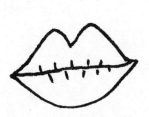

The Choosy Princess

Clare found this poem in a robin's nest.

The Choosy Princess wanted only the best,
So she set all her princes a puzzling
   quest . . .

"You must find me the bird
With invisible wings,
The spear of a flower,
The time-telling rings,
And the bright, golden kingdom
Without any kings."

The princes rode off down the long,
   winding track,
But none of them, none of them, ever
   came back.

The Choosy Princess took her crown from
the shelf.
"If the task is so tricky, I'll try it myself.

I'll search for the bird
With invisible wings,
The spear of a flower,
The time-telling rings,
And the bright, golden kingdom
Without any kings."

She strolled round the lawns with the
gardener's son,
They looked for her treasures and found
EVERY one.

"My puzzle was simple. The task was quite
small,"
She laughed as she happily counted them
all.

"Here's the egg of a songbird,
(With no wings to see!)
The thorn of a rosebush,
The rings of a tree,
And a sweet, golden comb
From the hive of a bee."

Then she married the boy she had loved all
    along –
The gardener's boy, who was clever and
    strong.

Princess Kat de Whisker

Clare found this poem in a cosy corner of the palace kitchen.

Princess Kat de Whisker
Prowls across the floor,
A panther snarls beside her,
A tiger guards her door.

Her robes are striped and slinky,
They flick like angry tails,
Her velvet gloves have holes to fit
Her spiky, silver nails.

Princess Kat de Whisker
Pads across the hall
To stroke the cook's old tomcat,
(She loves him best of all).

The Princess's Puzzle
An Acrostic

Clare found this poem in the Princess's pencil box.

Pearly and pale
As a sugary cake,
Lost in the mists of
A fairy-tale lake
Carved from the wishes
Each dreamer must make.

Answer: Run your finger down the line –
Find a PALACE fair and fine.

What the Sleeping Beauty Dreamed

Clare found this poem tangled inside a spider's web.

She dreamed of rooms where danger spins,
She dreamed of guards with sleepy grins.

She dreamed of time that ticked and flew,
She dreamed of thorns that thickly grew.

She dreamed of hopes that drift and fade,
She dreamed of princes. Lost. Afraid.

She dreamed of someone handsome, who
Could beat the brambles, battle through
And weave his way past cobwebs too.

She woke – and found that dreams come
true.

The Song of the Sorrowful Prince

Clare heard someone singing this song by the seashore.

A young prince sang on the sorrowful
   sands,
"I would give my castle, my treasure, my
   lands
And my father's crown of silver and pearl
To marry my gentle, my green-eyed girl."

But the waves replied with a sorrowful
    swirl,
"She is lost forever, your green-eyed girl.
She was whirled away on the morning tide,
For today she became the Sea King's
    bride."

Yet still he sings on the sorrowful sands,
"I would give my castle, my treasure, my
    lands
And my father's crown of silver and pearl
To marry my gentle, my green-eyed girl."

The Princess's Own Poem

Clare was given this poem by the Princess herself.

I'm not too pretty,
Not TOO plain.
I HATE glass slippers.
Quite like rain.
I love to dance
All night. And sing.
And balance on
A dragon's wing.
Or fly my carpet
Through the skies.
Or eat ice cream
With pumpkin pies.
I don't mind peas
(But wouldn't miss them).
I'm fond of frogs
(But never kiss them).
I LOVE my bouncy
Feather bed,
The silver crown
Upon my head . . .

But story tellers
Say I should
Be sweet and kind
And ALWAYS good –
So sometimes
(This is strange
Yet true)
I'd swap my gold
And palace too
To run away
And play with YOU.

Treasure

Clare found this poem in an old dog's cosy basket.

The Princess's dog had eyes as sharp as
    spindles
And a tail that wagged like a royal flag.

By night, he guarded her door as fiercely
    as a dragon
Even though he was no bigger
Than a dungeon rat.
And he feared no one,
Not even the palace soldiers
In their clumping iron boots.

The Princess called him Treasure.
She smoothed his bristly coat
With a mermaid's lost comb,
And whenever she visited the Wide World,
He sat beside her in the royal carriage.

His glossy nose could sniff, sniff, sniff
The one true prince
In a crowd of thousands,
And he was never once fooled
By a tattered coat
Or a broken, wooden sword.

A Row of Royal Limericks

The Royal Jester told Clare these poems.

The Princess of Now-or-Never
Was told to marry Prince Clever,
But the jester's son
Was far more fun –
They were happy for ever and ever.

The King of Misty Water
Had SUCH a grumpy daughter,
That (sad yet true)
He yelled, "YAHOOO!"
The day the dragon caught her.

The Princess of Dawn-and-Dew
Said, "Wishes NEVER come true."
A frog croaked, "Miss,
One tiny kiss
Will prove they SOMETIMES do!"

The Princess of Castle-So-Cold
Was keen to turn straw into gold,
A strange little man
Cried, "Nobody can!"
But she did. (Or at least – so I'm told.)

The Princess Belinda of Bore
Was keen to turn gold into straw.
When friends asked her why,
She said with a sigh,
"Because nobody's tried it before."

The Princess of So-Far-Away
Had never a word to say.
She lived all alone
In a tower of stone
And smiled at her mirror all day.

The Princess of Rubies-and-Rings
Tried wishing for magical things.
Her genie was new
(And short-sighted too)
So he gave her a tortoise with wings.

The Princess's Ball

Clare found this poem in the folds of a silky ball gown.

Watch them all whirl around,
    swirl around,
    twirl around,
Watch them all smile at the
    Princess's Ball.

Watch them all dance about,
    prance about,
    glance about,
Watch them all file through the
    shimmering hall.

Watch them all hurry by
    scurry by
    flurry by

Watch them all weave past the
          torches so bright.

Watch them all skip away,
          trip away,
          slip away,
Watch them all leave by the
          moon's magic light.

The Princess's Doll's House

Clare found this poem in the top turret of the doll's house.

The Princess's dolls
Have a palace of glass
With one broken turret
And lawns of real grass.
There are thousands of windows
With diamond panes
And painted grey horses
With long velvet manes.
There's a grumpy green dragon
Who sits on the stairs,
And roomfuls and roomfuls
Of small, golden chairs.
There's a colourful feast
On shiny blue dishes,
There's a ballroom, a bathroom,
A well (for your wishes),
And even a bedroom
Where Beauty can sleep,
And kitchens with fires,
And a dungeon (quite deep.)

And sometimes the Princess
Will wake in the night
To find that her palace
Is glowing with light!
And she's SURE she hears music
That joyfully comes
From tiny tin flutes
And singers and drums.
And she THINKS she sees people
Who dance up and down –
There's a girl like herself
In a little pink crown.

But then, in the morning,
Her dolls seem SO still
She says that she must
Have been dreaming. Or ill.
(But I'VE seen the mess
In the Banqueting Hall –
And I think the Princess
Was right, after all!)

The Beast's Little Joke

Clare found this poem in the Beast's garden shed.

"My Beauty's as sweet as can be,
(Though some of you may not agree).
She left me, then missed me,
She came back and kissed me . . .
And now – she's a Beastie like ME!"

I Hate Snow White
The Wicked Queen's Song.

Clare found this poem in the Wicked Queen's spell cupboard.

I hate Snow White,
Her pretty face
Around the place,
Her heart so light.

I hate Snow White,
I'll make her go
Where briars grow,
Where beasts will bite.

I hate Snow White,
She's safe once more!
I'll find her door,
So clean and bright.

I hate Snow White.
I'll watch her eat
My poisoned treat.
It serves her right.

I hate Snow White.
She's still as a stone
Yet not alone
By day nor night.

I hate Snow White.
My mirror tells
Of wedding bells . . .
I've lost the fight.

I HATE SNOW WHITE!

We Love Snow White

Clare found this poem inside the owl's hollow tree.

"We love Snow White,"
The guards agree.
"We'll cheat the Queen
And set her free."

"We love Snow White,"
The songbirds call.
"Her gentle voice,
Her hands so small."

"We love Snow White,"
The dwarfs all cry.
"We'll keep her safe.
She shall not die."

"We love Snow White,"
The creatures say.
"We'll find a prince
And lead the way."

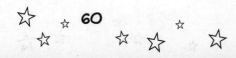

"I love Snow White,"
The young Prince sighs.
"I love her smile,
Her sparkling eyes."

"I love my friends,"
Snow White replies.
"The brave, the kind,
The good, the wise."

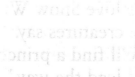

Grumpy

Clare found this poem under Grumpy's pillow.

When the dwarfs come home to their
    sleepy guest,
And they let her stay, and they let her rest,
It is Grumpy who, with a loud "NO! NO!"
Wants to throw her out. Wants to see her go.

When the Bad Queen comes to their tiny
    door,
And they find Snow White on the cold,
    cold floor,
It is Grumpy who, with a "She's not dead!"
Sings an angry song by her glassy bed.

When the handsome Prince finds his future
    wife,
And with one sweet kiss brings her back to
    life,
I believe I know (and I think you've guessed)
Who will miss her most, and who loves her
    best . . .
It's the one with GRUMPY on his proud,
    old chest.

The Princess's Crown

Clare found this poem tucked inside the lining of a small crown.

Look at the points that glitter and shine,
Look at the jewels from mountain and
   mine,
Look at the silver so fragile and fine,
Look at the trimming of snowy white
   down,
Look at my beautiful, second-best crown.

Aladdin's Princess

Clare found this poem beside an old brass lamp.

Aladdin's Princess is fond of secrets.
Her face is hidden by a veil of midnight-
    purple
Scattered with white stars,
And when she rides through the town
On her stately camel
Masked men guard her with glittering
    blades.

Her home is the mighty Palace of
    Mysteries
Where golden domes glint
Like metal onions.
There are more windows than anyone can
    count,
And rooms that have never been visited
(Except by the squeaky bats).
There are so many spiral staircases,
Her servants are always dizzy,
And the Princess herself lives at the very
    top
Of the twistiest tower.

All day she gazes down at her people
And dreams of the future.
Her father has chosen a fine prince for
  her –
A handsome man with a hundred camels
And a whole city of embroidered tents.

But she has already spied Aladdin,
With his friendly wave
And his enchanted lamp.

Her magic carpet is awake.
She is ready to fly.

The Beast's Palace

Clare found this poem underneath a talking clock.

The Beast's Palace was full of wonders.

A room where every single thing
Was made of rainbow-glass,
Even the floorboards
And the flames in the fireplace.

A room that fitted inside a room
That fitted inside a room
That fitted inside a room.

A room where the branchy throne,
The carpet of blue flowers,
The moss-green cushions
And the leafy curtains
Were all alive
And growing, growing.

A room where the clocks wore gloves
On their busy hands,
The chairs had cuddly arms,
And the friendly footstools scampered
 around
In fluffy slippers.

A room where Beauty saw herself
And a handsome prince
Reflected again and again
In its wall of mirrors.

A quiet room
Where she wanted to stay forever.
A lonely room
Where she longed for home,
And one, tiny room
Inside her own heart
Where the Beast could hide
If ever he dared to ask.

Mirror, Mirror

A Magic Mirror sang this song to Clare.

Mirror, mirror,
On the wall –
Will I glitter
At the ball?

Mirror, mirror,
Framed with gold –
Will my Prince
Be brave and bold?

Mirror, mirror,
Wise and true –
Will I be
A hero too?

Mirror, mirror,
Kind and tame, –
Will the dragons
Fear my name?

Mirror, mirror,
On the wall –
Will my deeds
Be praised by all?

Then the Mirror,
With a glare
grumbled, "Yes . . .
Now, comb your hair."

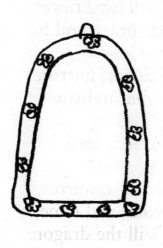

The Dragon Rap

Clare found this poem scorched on the walls of an empty cave.

Well, I ride the skies
On my flip-flap wings
And I scorch the air
And I scare the kings,
As I scan their lands
For a sweet princess
In her small, pink shoes
And her long, pink dress.
Then I breathe blue smoke
As I swoop and swirl
And I search the Earth
For a perfect girl.
Now, she can't be scared
And she can't be shy
And she can't be cross
And I'll tell you why . . .
See, I don't want tea
And I don't want lunch
And I don't want bones
I can munch and crunch.

No, I want a girl
Who is good and kind,
Who can sing old songs,
Who can read my mind,
Who can tell old tales
When I weep hot tears,
Who can kiss my nose
And my droopy ears,
Who can break the spell
That the bad witch cast,
Who can change me back
To a PRINCE at last!
So I'll flip and flap
Through the lonely skies
Till I find the girl
Who is brave and wise.

Cinderella's Poem

Clare found this poem inside a tiny glass dancing shoe.

I'm a shy girl,
A sigh girl,
A weary-wonder-why girl.
A poor girl,
A sore girl,
A sleep-upon-the-floor girl.

I'm a small girl,
A shawl girl,
A dream-about-the-ball girl.
A YES girl,
SUCCESS girl,
A lovely-magic-dress girl.

I'm a dance girl,
A chance girl,
To-catch-the-Prince's-glance girl.
A new girl,
A shoe girl,
A wishes-can-come-true girl.

A PRINCE-AND-PALACE-TOO GIRL!

The Real Princess

Or: The Princess and the Pea

Clare was told this story one dark and stormy night.

Oh, how the rainstorm broke with a roar,
Oh, how it rattled the old castle door.

One lost girl, dripping wet
On the palace doorstep. Yet
Hear her voice so weak and thin,
"I'm a Princess. Let me in!"

Oh, how Prince Lonely sighed when he
    saw her,
Oh, how he cried, "I shall always adore
    her."

He held her hand, he led her in,
Wiped the rain from nose and chin,
Drew her close to cosy flames
Begged to know her royal names.

Oh, how Queen Careful sniffed as she said,
"Oh, how she shivers. We'll send her to
    bed."

Can she pass the Princess Test?
Sleep upon a feather nest
Higher than a holly tree,
And underneath it all – ONE PEA!

Oh, how the stranger sobbed in the night,
Oh, how she longed for the day, and the
 light.

"Someone filled my sheets with stones,
Bruised my skin and bumped my bones,
Made me hurt from heel to head,
Horrid, hateful nasty bed."

Oh, how her words grew weary and wild,
Oh, how the Queen quite suddenly smiled.

"One small pea has proved you true –
You're a Princess through and through."
Cried the Prince, "Of course. Hooray!
Marry me. At once. Today."

Oh, how he changed from Lonely to
    Laughter,
And oh, how they lived warm and dry
    EVER AFTER.

The Naughty Princess

This poem was sung to Clare by the Princess's old nurse.

The Naughty Princess
Doesn't care, doesn't care
About lovely, long dresses
Or brushing her hair,
Or twiddly, fiddly
Bracelets to wear.

The Naughty Princess
Doesn't choose, doesn't choose
A golden tiara,
Or glittery shoes,
Or shimmery, glimmery
Coaches to use.

The Naughty Princess
Doesn't play, doesn't play
Sweetly and softly.
She's noisy all day,
She's sunny and fun and . . .
We like her that way!

The Dreamy Princess

Clare found this poem underneath a floppy teddy bear.

Her castle is a caravan.
Her throne's a wooden chair.
Her crown's a cosy bobble hat
That hides her silky hair.

Her dress is neatly mended
To cover up the tear.
Her treasure is a china cup
And one old teddy bear.

Her ballroom is an icy pond.
She has no gold to wear –
But when she reads her storybook
She simply DOESN'T CARE!

The Princess's Maths Lesson

Clare found this poem inside a royal maths book.

Little Princesses have maths lessons too,
And lists to remember – just like you!

How many years
Can a princess sleep?
How many steps
Has a staircase (steep)?
How many wishes
Are given away?
How many dancers
Skip out to play?
How many swans
Are seen in the sky?
How many carpets
Flutter and fly?
How many dwarfs
Have met Snow White?
How many lamps
Are shiny bright?
How many sisters
Are fierce and mean?

How many mirrors
Talk to a queen?
How many slippers
Are lost (then found?)
And how many dragons
Swoop around?

Add them together and what do you get?
Hundreds and hundreds and hundreds, I
  bet!

$1 + 6 =$
$\times 12 =$

$64 + 21 =$
$+ 2 \times 1 =$

The Surprise

Clare found this poem inside a magician's hat.

The Princess chewed her thumbnail,
Then wrote (with her curliest
Swirliest feather pen)
"For my birthday I would like
One surprising thing
That has never belonged to anyone else
Ever before."

"Oh dear," said the King and Queen,
Wobbling their crowns
In an anxious way.
The Princess already owned
ALL their best treasures.

An invisible robe.
(It had once belonged to her grandfather.)
A talking book that knew all the stories in
    the world.
(It had once belonged to a wizard.)
A silver bird that could lay sugar eggs.
(It had once belonged to a kindly giant.)
A purse of golden coins that was never

empty
However many times it was opened.
(It had once belonged to a tooth fairy.)
And a magic mirror that ALWAYS made
    her look lovely.
(It had once belonged to a good witch.)

"How can we surprise our little Princess?"
Sighed the King and Queen,
(Who were not as rich as you might
    suppose).
But the Magician's boy
Winked one eye.
"I think I know
If you'll let me try."

On the Princess's birthday
He placed a yellow party hat
At the foot of the royal bed
And sneaked away down the creaky stairs.
The Princess frowned at her paper crown.
"Perhaps I don't like surprises
After all," she grumbled.
But as she reached to grab it
Out popped, out popped . . .
A very small surprise
With silky, white ears

And a label that said –

'My name is BOO!
And I am just for YOU."

Rapunzel

Clare found this poem under the stones of a ruined tower.

Think of Rapunzel,
Trapped in her tower,
Held by a witch's
Invisible power.

Think of Rapunzel,
No ladder. No stair.
Only her tangly
Dangly hair.

Think of Rapunzel,
Think of the prince,
Tugging her tresses,
Making her wince.

Think of Rapunzel,
How she must cry,
"Send me a hero
Who knows how to fly!"

The Princess's Letter

Clare found this poem tied to a skylark's leg.

To: The King and Queen of Gloom—
   On—Water,
A message from your missing
   daughter . . .

> Who wants castles?
> Who wants kings?
> I like friends
> With leather wings.
>
> Who wants princes
> Strong and brave?
> I prefer a
> Cosy cave.
>
> Who wants crowns
> Of shiny gold?
> I like treasure
> Strange and old.

Who wants safe
And grassy ground?
I prefer to
Flap around.

Who wants heroes?
Not me! No!
Life is fun.
Don't want to go.

Dragon Hill's
The place to be,
Lots of love
From Sparks and Me.

X X X

TO THE
king and
Queen
of gloom
on
water
a message
from your

Dragon's Tale

When the Dragon of Dread dragged the
   Princess away
Over the wild, mountain passes
To the horrible cavern that smouldered all
   day
And scorched all the trees and the
   grasses . . .

She biffed him and bashed him until he
   turned grey,
She polished her small, misty glasses,
Then she biffed him again and said, "Sorry.
   Can't stay.
I'm missing my self-defence classes."

Palace Glossary

If some of these poems puzzle you, then perhaps these stories can help:

The Eleven Swans

This is an exciting but scary story. Eleven princes are put under an awful spell. Every dawn they change into swans and only their brave sister, Elise, can save them. She must make eleven shirts from stinging nettles (nasty!) and she must not speak one word until she has finished. A kind prince falls in love with her, but his people think she is a wicked witch and they want to kill her. Just in time, the swans swoop down and she throws her magic shirts over them. The spell is broken, she can speak again, and of course she marries her prince. (But the eleventh shirt only has one sleeve, so her favourite brother has one white wing forever.)

The Twelve Dancing Princesses

Twelve naughty sisters spoil their dancing shoes EVERY night – but how? Nobody knows until a poor soldier discovers their secret. He has a Cloak of Invisibility (given to him by a good witch) and he puts it on at midnight. Then he follows the princesses as they sail away in magical boats to a glittery island – and dance ALL night. The soldier tells the King and wins the reward. His prize is a princess . . . but which one will it be?

The Frog Prince

A spoiled princess loses her ball in a pond, and a helpful frog finds it for her. As a reward, he asks for a goodnight kiss. At first she agrees, but when he hops into the palace she very nearly breaks her promise. It's a good thing she doesn't because . . . he's a prince in disguise!

Princess Raven Wing

I have never seen this story anywhere before, so I can't tell you much about it. But I'm glad the princess found the enchanted king and broke the spell. I wonder if YOU have ever found a rusty old key . . . ?

Thumbelina

In the story books, Thumbelina is a tiny girl who is found inside a tulip. Because she is SO small, her life is full of frightening adventures. She is kidnapped by frogs, stolen by stag beetles and saved by a furry field mouse. Then a funny old mole falls in love with her! Luckily her best friend is a swallow who flies away with her to a magic land – where she marries the Flower King. (But in my poem the tiny Princess marries a mouse prince because I am very fond of mice.)

MATCHES